Robert John Auton
Born in Yorkshire in the late 20th century
Lover of creativity and the human side
of the human race

In Heaven
The Onions Make
You Laugh

Rob Auton

Illustrated by the Author

Burning Eye

With optimism and imagination
We know that, regardless of our plight
We always have the power
To create our own happiness

Wayne Coyne

LADIES AND GENTLEMEN

THESE ARE THE NAMES
WE GIVE TO
THE TOILETS.

Agenda

Orange and opinionless
That's what I expect from a carrot

Witty remarks and compliments
That's what I want from a parrot

Comfortable and defeated
That's what I expect from a sheepskin rug

Criminals losing hands
That's what I want from the millennium bug

Keith Moon giving the Queen Mother a drumming lesson
That's what I expect from a séance with my friends

The Earth wrapped in waterproof paper
That's the kind of present that I want to send

A computer desk made from the bones of the cruellest dragon
that ever lived
That's what I expect to buy from the Ikea store

A circumcised ant shouting orders at his troops
That's what I want from a holy war

Thunder clouds eating trees with forks of lightning
That's what I expect from Ready Steady Cook

A pigeon leaving a vapour trail
That's what I want to see when I look

The Sound Of The Umbilical Cord

After twelve hours of labour the baby was born. The nurse cradled the newborn in her latexed hands for a split second before it floated effortlessly to the ceiling of the delivery room. The mother screamed and began to tug helplessly at the unusually long umbilical cord, fast becoming as tight as a finely tuned guitar string. The baby screamed as its tears rained down onto the mother's sweat wet face.

Oh dear, said the nurse, gravity has chosen to ignore your baby.

Pardon me? Well, well, just what am I supposed to do? Asked the mother.

There are two options, we can cut the umbilical cord now and your baby will be free to float away out of your life forever, or we choose not to cut the cord and you remain attached to your baby. You will be the spaceship to your astronaut, the anchor to your ship, the kite flyer to your kite.

The nurse did not cut the cord, the baby went home with the mother. The mother walked home like a child going home with a balloon after visiting the fair, but her balloon was a baby. Over the years the baby grew and became a child, the child grew and became a teenager, forcing the cord to become tighter and tighter and tighter. Until one day the mother's feet left the ground forever.

Grim Genie

I rubbed the golden magic lamp with my palm and the Grim Reaper appeared in a puff of smoke.

Oh, I was rather hoping for a genie, I said.

I am working as a genie from today, as I was recently made redundant as Death, he said, looking at the ground with his hood covering his face.

Well I only have one wish and that is to die, I replied.

Death stared me in the face and began to sob.

Doors

One door closes, another door… closes.

One door closes, another door opens and another door closes.

One door opens, another door opens, another door opens, another door opens, another door opens, then five more doors open but you are too slow making your decision so they all simultaneously slam in your face.

One door opens, another door closes, one door opens and you jump through it then look back at the door and see that it is shut again.

You want to get back through but you can't.

You look around for other doors but there are only doorframes in this new environment that you are in. Why walk through a doorframe?

Suddenly the doorframes have doors and you really want to walk through them now but you can't because they all have signs on them and the signs say CLOSED and you don't question the signs. You could check the doors but you are too busy thinking about a new shiny door that is surrounded by light bulbs like a mirror in Dolly Parton's dressing room.

One door opens, another door closes, another door opens, another door opens but you ignore them all because you are focussed on this door. The Dolly door. This is the door. This is the door to your future. The one you need to get through more than any other. After this door every other door will just be a door. You bang on the Dolly door until the Dolly door opens and Dolly Parton is there and she's got doors for eyes and a door for a nose and small black doors for nostrils and a double door for a mouth and hundreds of yellow doors for hair and you can't decide which of Dolly's doors you want to go through.

Her eyes open and shut like they are blinking at you, you think she is flirting so you walk through her mouth and you instantly wish you had gone through her nose. You are in her mouth and her tongue is a fleshy pink trapdoor, her teeth are white doors and you think about all these new doors that could open to you but you just stand there and hope that they open for you instead of kicking them down.

One door opens, another door opens, another door closes, you find someone who is looking for the same doors as you, you begin to walk through the doors together and it isn't quite as hard as before. You find humour in the doors, you find love in the doors, you find children in the doors, you find life in the doors.

One door closes, another door opens, and the lid of your coffin slams shut.

Another door opens and you are in Heaven and all the doors in front of you are open. You start to think about how good it was to have closed doors.

Doors with something behind them.

Ring Ing Ing Ring Ing Ing

Ring a ring a ringtone
A pocket full of telephone
I'll call you
I'll call you
So we can have a row

Father And Son

If I have a son
His name will be Dad
After my Dad, and his Dad, and his Dad, and his Dad, and his
Dad
At the hospital I will introduce Dad to my Mum
Mum this is Dad, your Grandson
Don't cry Dad, it's Mum, your Grandma
On Christmas Eve I will say to him
You better get to bed soon Dad or Father Christmas won't come
And he will be confused but not as confused as me
As he grows up other children will call him by his name and my
son will become the father figure of the playground
PASS ME THE BALL DAD
My Mum said you can come round to my house for tea tonight
Dad
At morning registration his teacher will call him by his name in
a voice of complete and utter tenderness
Dad

Sharing A Yoghurt With God

We sat next to each other on my living room floor on a red bean-bag, God's vast weight forcing my side of the bag to become fit to burst. The stitching hadn't expected such difficult tests from God of all people. I held a yoghurt in my hand, a Muller Strawberry Crumble Corner. I peeled off the plastic fake foil lid, licked it, then folded it diagonally in half and placed it on the newly hoovered carpet.

God motioned his hand over mine, my grip of the yoghurt suddenly became loose and began to hover in the air between us. Each possessing a spoon, God's was golden, mine was of the free white plastic variety. I sunk my spoon into the virgin yoghurt as God dug his into the crunchy biscuit novelty corner. He raised his golden spoon with egg and spoon race care and shovelled the bone-dry biscuit crumbs passed the bright of his Tic Tac teeth and into his mouth.

What are you doing? I cried. You can't eat all the biscuit, I like the biscuit. We are meant to mix it up, I can't believe it.

God looked at me, his beard now sewn with seeds of biscuit. Emotion free, unforgiving eyes. A St Christopher earring hung still from his hairy scrotum lobe.

God moved his head toward the floating yoghurt as if he was going to smell it, but slowly released a paste of biscuit and saliva perfect in consistency onto the white yoghurt.

It rested turd like on the smooth ripple-less surface and slowly began to sink.

God raised his snarling head and wiped his mouth.

I looked him in his greying eyes and rose from the beanbag.

BACON

Francis Bacon and Kevin Bacon are the rashers from
a very talented pig
The pig could paint
The pig could act
The pig was a genius as a matter of fact

Zzzzzzzorro

Now ninety one years of age, the once almighty Zorro shuffles slowly down the corridors of the retirement home, walking stick in one hand, shaking sword in the other. His faded jet black mask hangs grey and slack from his face, frayed at the edges like the wings of a thousand year old bat. In the dead of night he creeps silently into the rooms of his fellow residents and makes Z shapes in the air above their heads as they sleep, reminding him of days gone by.

See, Kiss, Marry

Climb onto my bones
Soak your jeans crimson as you space hop on my heart

Explore the village of me
I will be sailing down the red river of the main artery in your
right leg
In a knackered canoe
Water sliding down the rapids of your large intestine on a
garden refuse sack
Wandering the pink walled maze of your thought graffitied
brain

Let's tuck ourselves in under each other's skin
Using thoughts of the future as hot water bottles

Susan

The only words that Susan knew how to say were the titles of her favourite films

She would say them to me to inform me of her current mood

If she was angry she would shout, GORRILAS IN THE MIST

If she was depressed she would quietly whisper, Schindler's List

If Susan was feeling a bit trapped in the relationship but optimistic that it would have a happy ending she would say, Shawshank Redemption

If I wanted to make love to her, but it was that time of the month, she would snap at me the name of any period drama

But when my birthday came around she did not have to think, she would simply say the words, Basic Instinct

Carspotter

I spot cars
I am a carspotter
I stand on the side of the road and write down number plates
If it's a busy road I don't write down the number plate
I just say
There's one
There's one
There's one
If the roads are really busy I say
There's two
There's two
There's two
Sometimes if the roads are really, really busy
I don't even say there's two
I just say YES
YES
YES
YES
When I was little my parents took me on holiday to the M1
I am a carspotter, my favourite type of jam is traffic
I like to sit in parks that have tarmac instead of grass and cars
instead of trees

Tarmacced

Today
The roads were tarmacced
The pavements were tarmacced
The hills were tarmacced
The mountains were tarmacced
The fields were tarmacced
The rivers were drained and then tarmacced
The animals were put to sleep and then tarmacced
The flowers were tarmacced
The paintings were tarmacced
The music was tarmacced
The forests were chopped down and then tarmacced
The clouds were tarmacced
The sky was tarmacced
The moon was tarmacced
The sun was tarmacced

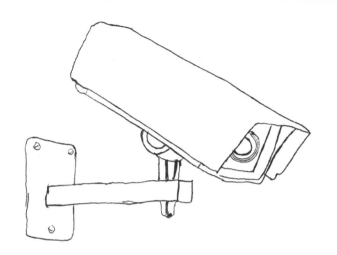

WHEN I WAS
LITTLE
I THOUGHT
CCTV WAS A
VERY POSITIVE
SPANISH
TV CHANNEL.

Tai Chi Chai Tea Chai Tai Chi Tea

I attempt to drink my Chai Tea as I practice my Tai Chi
My Chai Tea is getting in the way of my Tai Chi
I keep spilling my Chai Tea on my Tai Chi mat
Making my Tai Chi mat smell of Chai Tea
It has become a Chai Tea Tai Chi mat

Maroon

The painters have painted ma room maroon
The painters have painted ma room maroon
Ma room ma room ma room's maroon
I've got a maroon room
I'M MAROONED in a room of MAROON

The walls of ma room are maroon
The floor of ma room is maroon
The curtains of ma room are maroon
It's so maroon it's ruined ma room
Give me back ma room paint away the maroon

I look up to my clock and see that the painters have spilt quite
a big dollop of maroon paint over the 12 of my clock
The painters have painted ma noon maroon
The painters have painted ma noon maroon
Ma noon, ma noon, ma noon's maroon
I've got a maroon noon

I tear down my maroon curtains and I look up to the moon
The painters have painted ma moon maroon
The painters have painted ma moon maroon
Ma moon ma moon ma moon's maroon
I've got a maroon moon
The man on the moon is dressed in maroon
The cow jumping over the moon's maroon
The sky surrounding the moon's maroon
The moon is marooned in a sky of maroon
I'm marooned in a world of maroon

Bread Sandwich

Two slices of white sliced bread with a baguette in the middle
Bread sauce instead of butter
Coated in breadcrumbs
Garnished with croutons
Eaten with breadsticks
Served on a bread board
Stored in a bread bin

Depressed

How do you spell depressed?
Well it starts with a d I suppose
You know that letter that spells out the beginning of death
Then take an e
You can take as many e's as you like you are still going to die
Then put pressed on the end
You know like a dream gets pressed tightly into a dustbin by
the foot of a boss

PEOPLE REALLY LISTEN TO THEIR PILLOWS.

Near Reincarnation

At the supermarket I bought
200 packets of smoked bacon
200 packets of unsmoked bacon
24 packets of Lincolnshire sausages
150 pork chops
25 packets of pork belly
46 slices of gammon
12 packets of wafer thin honey roast ham and 16 joints of ham

Returning home I put my glue gun on to heat, unpacked all the meat and laid it out on several cut open dustbin bags on my garage floor. When the glue gun reached its temperature I began to stick the meat together creating a sculpture of an adult pig. Millimetres of meat cooked from the heat of molten glue.

After two hours of clumsily fixing flesh, the animal began to take shape. Four fat fleshy trunk legs created from the joints of ham. Belly pork glued where belly pork should be. Sausages for intestines. Using cheap honey roast ham for the ears, they were floppy and unpricked. I looked at the pig made from pork and wrapped it in cling film.

I then returned to the supermarket and bought large amounts of lamb chops, lamb shoulders, cutlets, shanks, legs and repeated the process. When the lamb was finished I bought chicken. Chicken thighs, drumsticks, breasts, wings. When the chicken was finished I bought beef and so on until after three days of intense creativity my garage resembled a butcher's farmyard. I played animal sounds through an old paint splattered cassette player and invited my friends over to show them what I had been doing with my time off from the accountants.

Earth Potato

Have a nice day, said the shopkeeper.

I'll try, I replied.

Yes it's hot out there today isn't it, said the shopkeeper.

Too hot, I replied.

It's hot like a hot potato out there today isn't it, said the shopkeeper.

Pardon?

The weather, the weather is hot, like a hot potato.

What are you trying to say? You think the world is like a hot potato and I can't keep hold of it? You think that I keep losing my grip of reality and dropping reality only to pick it up again off the floor and burn myself?

No, the weather, it's hot, like a potato is hot.

The weather is nothing like a potato. They look completely different. A potato is almost round and the weather, the weather doesn't have a shape.

No but the Earth has a shape and the Earth feels like a hot potato today, said the shopkeeper.

I picked up my shopping without losing eye contact and began to back away. I walked through the automatic doors thinking about digging into the hot potato of the world with a shovel and burying myself alive in its mash.

Animal

I saw an animal coated in enamel
The enamel coated animal was a camel
The enamel coated animal camel left enamel coated animal
camel footprints
I followed the enamel coated animal camel footprints to a castle
In the castle lived a giant foot
The foot was the Foot Prince
I followed the footprints to the Foot Prince
The Foot Prince shouted, GET THOSE ENAMEL COATED
ANIMAL CAMEL FOOTPRINTS OFF MY FLOOR

Swimmers

I like to pretend that everybody I ever see has just been swimming
In a swimming pool
It makes me feel safer around people
You don't go swimming in a swimming pool and then mug
somebody
Oh she's just been swimming
That must have been lovely for her
That look that people possess when they walk out of the
swimming baths
With their endorphins dolphining around their upright again
bodies
They are pumped, inflated, eager to tread concrete
As if the water was their huge wet battery charger
There is one lady who I see most mornings
She has the most perfectly dry hair for someone who has just
been swimming
To achieve such dryness she must dry each hair on her head
individually, with a fresh towel for each hair
I pair people up with a stroke
And watch them swim effortlessly around my mind
Where there is no bombing

Key

As he got up to leave the train
A small gold key fell from his pocket
I picked it up, Sorry, is this yours?
He looked at the key, Oh thanks
No expression, or maybe that was his happy face
His *Oh my God I can't believe I nearly lost that key* face
I began to imagine what the small gold key was for
A window he hated opening
An empty safe
Or maybe it was a key he had been trying to lose
Dropping it again and again
People forever picking it up and giving it back to him
If I hadn't picked it up I might have made his day

Poem About A Kettle
(Written when listening to a lot of Leonard Cohen)

I filled my kettle with tears
The tears I stole from your eyes when you weren't looking
Clicked it on to boil
After a minute I could hear your distant weeping
With the heat came the cries
Before long the kitchen was full of bubbling screams
The kettle peaked, extinguishing the little light it had
I poured your sorrow onto the teabag of my life
And drank the sadness of your being

Waterproof

Look at that Duck
It's waterproof
Proof that water exists
Just like me

Satsuma

I ate a satsuma
In every single segment of that particular satsuma was a seed
A seed the size of a small sultana
It was as if each segment had been given the heart of a full satsuma
Supercharged segmentation
Would I feel more equipped to deal with life if I had more hearts?
Or would I be too emotional to go on?
A heart at the end of each of my fingers
A heart buried in each of my palms
A heart in my stomach
A heart in each of my lungs
A heart in my liver
Two hearts in my scrotum
Hearts instead of red blood cells
Hearts for teeth
A heart at the tip of my tongue
A heart in each of my earlobes
A heart in my brain
I would walk the streets a romantic beating mess
People would shake my hand and feel the beat of my hearts
Imagine how much you could love somebody with all those hearts
I am a satsuma with a single pip

A HILL IS A HILL,

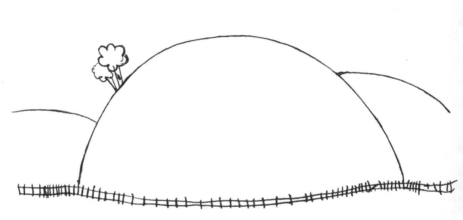

BECAUSE IT HASN'T BREATHED OUT YET.

Platform

I stand on King's Cross platform 4 waiting for my Mum to arrive on the 09:12 from Edinburgh. In my hands I hold a laminated A4 piece of white paper with the word MUM clearly printed in the middle. The train pulls in and the passengers alight, those who are not my Mum walk past me. Grown men read my sign and continue on their journeys. Ladies who fit the description look at me in a motherly way, they know that they are not my Mum but for a split second they think the sign might possibly be for them. I wait patiently until a lady sees the sign, smiles, and stops.

Skies

I grabbed the sky from the crisp winter morning
Screwed it into a bluebird
Threw it up into the empty air

I grabbed the sky from the overcast afternoon
Molded it into a soggy pigeon
Threw it up into the empty air

I grabbed the sky from the full moon night
Folded it into a star encrusted crow
Threw it up into the empty air

Three skies flying like birds

Teddy In The Jury Box

It's Valentine's Day and I am in court
Making notes about a rape case with a blunt pencil
I am juror number eleven
There are now eleven jurors in our jury
Juror number ten, the juror who sat to my left, fell asleep twice
when key pieces of evidence were being given
He fell asleep in the middle of her nightmare
And was excluded from the jury

I look at the wigs, the cloaks, the tape recorders, the red LEDS
on the tape recorders, the microphones, the carpet that looks
like it was made in black and white, the water jugs, the judge's
jewellery, the nose of the prosecution, the earlobes of the
defence
They all come together to make me realise where I am

I walk along the fleshy tightrope of life
A tightrope made from the small intestines of every human
that has ever lived

Today does not make sense
Rain is falling from the sun
The clouds are blue and the sky is grey
One minute oranges are hanging from trees
The next minute it's people

The inflated heart balloons I see on my way home seem to have
inflated themselves with the wind they took from my sails
The teddies in the card shops are stuffed with my confusion
about the case
They sit with a fixed expression
Just like I do in court

Hope

Every so often
Hope leaves me
Lets go of my hand
I am reminded of this when I hold a freshly photocopied
piece of paper up to my face
The warmth pulls the lids over my eyes
But slowly it backs away into the shadows
It no longer possesses the magic
The heat
The hope

Footballer's Life For Me

I work in an art supplies shop
I get paid £250,000 a week
Crowds of screaming fans gather at the windows of the shop
Wearing replicas of my staff T-shirt that say STAFF on the back
They cheer me on with my daily tasks through chant and song
Stack those paint pots, stack those paint pots, stack those paint
pots and sell them, stack those paint pots and sell them

If I sell a particularly expensive set of oil paints the cheers can
be heard right across Soho

Young children copy my unique method of stocktaking
masking tape and rival art shops bid to get me on their books
of watercolour paper

The injuries I suffer at work such as paper cuts from cardboard
boxes
Are dealt with on the spot by the staff physio
Are you sure that you can continue to work today Rob? Asks
the physio
Yes I can continue, I reply, to the delight of my screaming fans
at the window

TV stations fight for the rights to televise footage from the
shops CCTV cameras
So the nation can see how I collapse a cardboard box
Or inform a customer
Yes Madam, I'm sorry, these are the only colours of pencil
sharpeners that we sell

Downside Up

The upside down pint glass is an empty pint
The upside down trilby is a collection box without a lid
The upside down fly is dead
Dead lucky to be able to perform such aerial acrobatics
To be upside down is to turn something on its head
If something doesn't have a head it can still be upside down
When the upside is down

A pea is never upside down
Even if a pea was upside down nobody could tell
I envy the freedom of objects that can go unnoticed when
upside down
They sit free from judgement
A lump of mud
A logoless golf ball
A floating bubble
A piece of fluff

When I feel upside down people say, What's wrong with you?
You look terrible
I stand there and say, I'm OK, wishing I was a Rubik's Cube

THE MONSTER
WITH
BUNTING
FOR TEETH

Goose Bumps

I touched your naked arm in the cold of the night and read the braille of your goose bumps as you slept. I moved my hand gently across your arm and a vivid picture of your dream was painted.

You are on your way to the Jobcentre in Walthamstow, it's overcast and planted stars sit nestled in the underbelly of the bruised clouds like currants in scones twinkling in the midday greyness. Dark diamonds floating in puffs of concrete. Old-fashioned cars hmmmmm along navy blue carpeted roads almost silently, as jumbo jets flap their feathered wings overhead. Butterflies with wingspans of a metre swoop down, legs as thick as chopsticks. You approach the Jobcentre to find there is an elderly gentleman standing in front of the revolving door. He is costumed in a lime green top hat and tails. As you look down to see your face in each of his shoes a pristine white glove points the way inside. Classical music fills the air to the corners and lead balloons float effortlessly from the desk of each job advisor. A life drawing class takes place in the corner as decorated beauty queens hand out jobs in parcels delicately wrapped in tissue paper varying in size and colour.

You see me sat talking to a beautiful careers advisor, a spectacled secretarial porn star. She is running her ankle up and down my calf under the table as we talk about where I see myself in five years time. From over the top of her glasses she starts telling me where she sees me in five minutes time. She takes my hand and I follow her into a stationery cupboard with a disco ball and... suddenly you turn over and put your arm around me, your goose bumps begin to sink. I move away and start fanning your arm with a magazine to try and retrieve the dream. Only to wake you up. What are you doing? You ask sleepily. I throw the magazine to the floor and pretend to be asleep.

Coin Face

There lives a man in Bradford who ages as the Queen does
on coins
For long periods his face remains the same
But once every few years he suddenly becomes remarkably older
When this happens
People have heart attacks
If he has kept the same face for a number of years his loved
ones become nervous and attempt to prepare themselves for the
severe transformation
His wife employs police sketchers to give her an artist's
impression of what to expect and refuses to use her finest china

Vapour Tale

At first glance I believed it to be a vapour trail
I looked, and looked, and looked
Until it revealed itself to be not so much a vapour trail
But more of a very, very, very straight cloud

Nasty Nazi

It was Christmas time in 1942 as I walked through the snow caked streets of Berlin. In my gloved hand I held a hand drawn map detailing the whereabouts of Hitler's bunker. I followed the map carefully and eventually came to the address to find that it wasn't so much of a bunker, but more of a terraced house. Hesitating for a moment I rang the doorbell. The blood red wreathed door opened slowly.

Oh Rob it's you, you made it, I can't believe you actually made it, said Hitler.

Before I could say my hellos he was simultaneously pointing to both his moustache that he had clumsily died white, and to his top of the range crimson Santa hat that was falling over his eyes.

For the kids, he quipped.

Oh that's great you look exactly like him, I replied.

Well, well don't just stand there come in, come in.

We walked through into the living room, I noticed he had paper chains of white swastikas hanging from the ceiling.

That's my kind of snowflake, he said proudly with a puffed out chest, they took me all morning you know. Oh I almost forgot, said Hitler before disappearing upstairs.

I could really feel the difference with him being out of the room, more than anybody I had ever met. In the corner of the living room stood a white structure, it was shaped like a Christmas tree but wasn't quite there. On closer inspection the tree was made from what looked like human bones. Back bones for the trunk right through to finger tips at tips of branches. Actual size multi-coloured glass hand grenades and angels in paper SS uniforms jewelled the graceless branches. I could hear Hitler running down the stairs. I stood waiting for him with my hands by my sides.

Found it.

Before I knew it he had his hands behind his back playfully prompting me to pick one.

Ok left or right? Which one?

Oh no don't be silly, you didn't have to get me a present, I'm just happy that you asked me round for tea.

WHICH ONE? he shouted, LEFT OR RIGHT?
I began to tremble, I could feel warm urine beginning to make its way to the carpet via the inside of my thigh.
I pointed to his right ironed arm with my shaking index finger.
His face cracked back into a smile.
Good choice, he said.
With his right hand he presented me with a mahogany based snow shaker with a plastic cartoon character of himself inside and with his left hand he placed his revolver on the table.

Land Fish Sea Birds

The airborne and the sea life have swapped habitats

A crow flies slowly through the dark deep of the North Sea

A jellyfish pulses towards the midday sun
With light filling her translucent hood she resembles an
elaborately tasselled switched on floating lamp

Starfish suck at the ceiling of the sky as barnacles gather on
telegraph poles

In Trafalgar Square a blue whale bumps gently into Nelson and
changes direction

The wings of a humming bird are slow motioned as it dips its
beak into a coral reef searching for nectar
The bees are in the seas

The peck of a chicken stirs up the ocean floor

Butterflies glide like harmless tiny technicolor stingray

A sardine shoal stages an air show
Mirrored by the starlings of the sea

Flying fish don't know where to put themselves
Upside down and inside out

The beak of an albatross daggers out from the sea and into the
air plucking a bottom dwelling carp from the surface
With his catch he recoils from air into water

Perching on a mast of a sunken pirate ship a blackbird sings her
only hit, a tune caught in bubbles it rises to the surface and pops
into sound

Post A Card

I received a blank white postcard in the mail this morning
At least I thought it was blank until I turned it over and it read
Hi Rob, it's snowy here, love Mum and Dad

Blank white postcards
Postcards of snow
Cheap to print
Cheap to print
Stick them to the sky and watch it cloud over

Gandalf

My next door neighbours have a tortoise called Gandalf
I watch him from my bedroom window as he paces around
their back garden
He never sees me
Being called Gandalf I thought I would have seen him
perform a trick or two
I have never seen him perform any tricks
apart from being a tortoise
He is a one trick tortoise

WHERE THERE'S A WILL

THERE'S A DEAD PERSON.

Lid Licker

The way she licks the lid of the yoghurt
Represents her love of life
Not only does she lick the underside of the yoghurt lid, the side
often thinly layered with the white wet
She also licks the dry plastic business side
She revels in this as much if not more than when her tongue
washes in the dripping cow wax
She shuts her eyes tighter, really fist-clenches her eyelids closed,
her tongue grows flaccid and shiny like a massive pink melted
dripping diamond covered in clear olive oil

She licks the name, delighted by the fact that the yoghurt has
been given a name
She licks the letters that man came up with to label things such
as yoghurts
Each dot of an i a clitoris

She licks the logo and romanticises about the designers with
their pens and pencils
The studios they work in and how they probably have really
good Christmas parties

She drags her slippery, limp bottom lip over photographs of fruit
There is no taste but that's because there is very little taste when
licking an unbroken fruit with your bottom lip
She licks the use by date and thinks about the calendars in the
yoghurt factory and the factory workers and the cars of the
factory workers and the seats in the cars of the factory workers
and the radios and the people working for the radio stations and
the carpets of the radio stations and the thick glass windows in
the studios and the views from the windows of
the radio stations
The grass, the trees, the concrete, the buildings
She licks at life from the lid of the yoghurt
And digests it in the stomach of her imagination

Rollerball

Excuse me, do you work here?

Yes Sir I do

Oh great, I wonder if you can help me, I'm looking for a rollerball pen, but not just any rollerball pen, I want the ball in the end of the rollerball pen to be as big as the Earth

Do you sell such a product?

Yes Sir we do, you are standing on it

Oh fantastic and a rollerball of this size fits most pen shafts does it?

Yes Sir it does

Great I'll take one

You are lucky Sir, it's the last one in stock

Meeting A Vegetarian

I met a vegetarian
You're a vegetarian? So you don't eat bacon? I asked
What's bacon? She replied
You know bacon from pigs
Pigs? No, what are they?
I went on to list a comprehensive range of animals and the
meats that they produce and she could not recall a single one
We got into my car and I took her to a field full of cows and she
could not see them
A field full of cows to me
Was a field full of grass to her
As an atheist is an atheist because he or she can't see God
She was a vegetarian because she couldn't see meat

Mistake

Waiter you've made a mistake with mi steak
I asked for mi steak to be well done but this steak is rare

I apologise Sir, mistakes are rare in this restaurant

Well a mistake is what has been made in the kitchen
Instead of making mi steak you've made a mistake
I can make mi steaks properly, why can't you make mi steaks
properly?

I can make mistakes properly Sir, when you said
I want mi steak well done
I thought you wanted us to make a mistake, and do it well

Make a mistake well?
Make mi steak well done is what I wanted
So where is mi steak?

Your mistake is in front of you Sir

The Cat In The Window

The cat sits in the window of the first floor flat
Opposite from where I write
It is the exact same colour as the road below
So still it looks like a furry chunk of road
Complete with cats eyes
It is there every day, as I have been recently
A mirror image of something that is alive
I am writing about the cat
The cat is definitely not writing about me
If relaxed was a Russian doll
This cat would be the doll in the centre
Warm, sheltered, ambivalent to everything
There is something about a cat sitting in a window looking at
the world that makes humans seem absolutely ridiculous
I can see thought bubbles bubbling from triangular ears
He is in a car. Why bother?
It's raining. Unlucky.

Wave

Give me a wave, said the sand to the sea
Not just when you approach but when you leave
You wave hello with such purpose
But there is no wave in your goodbye
You cower and retreat back into the deep
As if you ran up to a beach you thought you knew
But when you realised it wasn't who you thought it was
You wanted the sea to swallow you up
And it did

Flour Power

You slid your hand down my throat with remarkable ease. I could feel you fiddling with my ventricles and other things, and then with a quick tug you whipped out my heart. I remained surprisingly conscious. You dropped it into your food processor with a tablespoon of flour and blended it until you had a pink plastercine like consistency. You then transferred it onto the work surface and moulded it into the shape of your new boyfriend.

Stars

The dead crouch down to the swept floor of Heaven each holding a pin, when it's dark enough on Earth they prick the paper thin floor of Heaven that doubles as the ceiling to our... thing. This allowing a tiny bit of Heaven to shine through. It looks bright up there. If it is that bright all the time how does anybody get any sleep? The electricity bill must be huge, having lights on like that all the time.

Breakfast

I knew the world outside had ended
When I poured milk on my Rice Crispies
And they made no sound

TRYING TO EAT AN APPLE BY LICKING IT.

Male Stationery

If I had a pen for a penis
I would write all over your face
I'd use your spots as punctuation
Not one blemish would I waste

If it was alright with you
I would fill your mouth with ink and use it as a quill
So when we go out to restaurants
I could indecently sign the bill

BNP

The moon is the new face of the British National Party. Party members can be seen to dance around in jubilation at the sight of the full moon. They stare down the barrel of a brand new piece of chalk on the blackboard of the night sky. Observing the moon cycle closely, their ecstasy is slowly transformed into anger as the face of their new leader loses its whiteness.
This is what is happening to our country, they bellow.

Religious Pets

My pets have turned to religion
My canary now wears a Burka
My rabbit made a crucifix in the wire mesh of her hutch with
two pieces of straw
One piece of straw is longer than the other
My cat goes out every Sunday morning and listens to another
cat that wears a dog collar
My guinea pig gathered his droppings together with his little
paws and used them to spell out the words
I PREFERRED IT ON THE ARK!
My tropical fish have started fasting
My dog now does everything backwards in an attempt to
inform me of the name of his new owner
What could I possibly have done to drive them to this?

Her

I look at you and see that parts of your face glitter and twinkle
Where some people have diamond piercings that shine in the light
You just have magical bits of your face

Angling Times

I am a boy fishing with his Dad
Mum is cooking Sunday dinner for when we are not fishing
When fishing you are among the first to realise it is raining
And the last to get indoors
Raindrops hammer our floats until the rain begins to bite
He pulls keepnet from water ring by ring by ring
Our tubular football goal of results
Fish emerge from the bottom of the murky washing up bowl
Stray forgotten spasming cutlery
A frantic slick motor of activity lifted from lake
Our caught afternoon tumbles down in time with the rain
The fish are fish again
Thighs of tracksuit bottoms wiped stiff with slime
Odd scattered scales turn me into a dressed down Merboy
We drive home listening to Chris Rea's *Road to Hell*
Soon to bite
Into beef

Diary Entry 24/9/82

It's 8:50pm on friday night and I've just been born
With the whole weekend in front of me
As well as my entire life
Yesterday I didn't officially exist
I've been crying quite a lot so far
It's not that I don't want to be here, it's just that, at the moment
It's the only thing that I know how to do properly

My first day on Earth and it's my birthday
What a coincidence
Friday seems like a good night to be born on
I'm not going to go out tonight because I don't know how
I heard a lady say "it's a boy" so I guess that's what I am
And what I will be for the rest of my life

I'm not sure what the plan for tomorrow is yet
I'll just take it one day at a time
I can't really remember yesterday and the day before that is
even more fuzzy
My heart is beating which is great
I haven't seen myself in the mirror yet
I wonder what I will look like when I am a full day old?
I hope I don't look too old when I am a day old
A day is a long time when you are only five minutes old

Body

I can't wait to see you tonight
You will bring your head with you won't you?
Yes I will, I know how much you like my head
And you will bring your arms with you won't you?
Yes I will bring my arms
Your arms with the hands on the ends?
Yes I will bring my arms with the hands on the ends
What about your legs? Will you bring your legs with you?
Listen with your ears, I will bring my whole body to your
house tonight
It's easier for me that way
My heart and brain will be in the exact same place at the exact
same time, like always
I will be in complete control of my face
Until I reach you

I AM HAPPY
LIKE A DOLPHIN
ON A T-SHIRT
WHEN IT GETS
PUT IN THE WASH.

I AM HAPPY LIKE HITLER WEARING NOTHING BUT A HAND GRENADE.

I AM SAD LIKE AN EASTENDERS FUNERAL ON CHRISTMAS DAY.

I AM HAPPY LIKE SALVADOR DALI WITH A PAINT BRUSH SHOVED DOWN THE END OF HIS PENIS.

I AM SAD LIKE AN ICE SCULPTURE OF MORRISSEY PRAYING FOR THE SUN TO COME OUT.

I AM HAPPY LIKE A
MATHEMATICIAN
EATING HIS
DINNER OFF
A NUMBER PLATE

I AM SAD
LIKE A DOG
CALLED CAT.

Drilling

A structure made from flesh and bone
My brain is the drill bit
Thoughts turn and press against the sky
I drill for happiness
I dream of striking the white of Heaven
Covering me in hope, drenching me in optimism
I search for Heaven on Earth and find it in the tiny

As often as I drill for Heaven, I unwillingly drill for Hell
Staring at the ground so hard, my thoughts pierce dirt until I
strike red
It bubbles, boils and sprays up out of the ground
Flames up like a Roman candle
I try to mask over the ruby of Hell with diamond thoughts of
Heaven
Red and white mix
Creating the colour of my skin
It is me left in the middle
Mixed race
Half Heaven, half Hell

Haunted

I am haunted by my own ghost
He sleeps at the end of my bed like a dead cat with a human's
haircut
I feel no fear towards him
He is me
I am him
Two sides of the same coin
Two sides of the same life
Why have you chosen to haunt me? I ask me
You've seen this all before
You must get bored of watching repeats?
Don't tell me what happens I haven't seen the end
Get out there, I tell me, live your death

He is a quiet ghost
Like he's had the wind knocked out of his guts
Maybe that's what death does to you
He looks at me with envy, leaves me messages in the steamed
up mirror when I'm in the shower
Vague, faint musings, the kind of thing you write when you
are drunk and think are brilliant until you discover them in the
morning

We watch television together and laugh in the same places
Listen to the same music and skip the same songs
We sleep and wake up at the same time
We get hungry at the same time and share the same taste in food
The difference being, I can taste it
I can feel the food in my mouth
I need it to live
He doesn't
For him it's a force of habit
I would rather have him haunt me than somebody else

Waiting With A Superhero

A middle-aged man sits opposite me in the doctor's surgery
He has a tattoo of a half peeled banana on his forearm
Could it be Bananaman?
Or is he just a very committed greengrocer?
What would Bananaman be doing in a doctor's surgery in
Walthamstow?
Superhero or not, he still has a tattoo of a half peeled banana
on his forearm and that warrants him the title of Bananaman

Clown In Flight

The clown rushed to work in his favourite Spitfire
Destination circus
Made up with thunder clouds around his eyes
The turbulence from the outer storm forced him to weep
Chubby tears fell from the eyes of his personal tempest
Collecting the white powder paint of his make up as they
rolled down his cheeks like vertical tumbleweeds
The tears ran from clear to pearl
Blunt ageing wings of plane cut sideways through dark moist
cake of night
Pale rubber gloves gripped shaking, rusting controls
Bald painted head reflected fresh sheets of lightning
Paused pink tornado curls of wig sat gently on lap
Showtime in fifteen minutes

Humans

On this night I am in need of scaffolding
May your bones be my scaffolding poles
I am the seat that needs to sit down
the map in need of directions
the cough sweet with the cough
the crutch with the broken leg
the kettle that would do anything for a cup of tea
the can of deodorant with B.O.
the road that dreams of travelling
the sleeping pill suffering from insomnia
the starving fork
the scissors that need a hair cut
the pump that needs inflating
the breast that craves a nipple to suckle on
the sun that longs to be shined on

Bricks Of The Sun

For Christmas I received a Lego sunset, on the box was a
printed photograph
A sunset from a far off land
Or it could have been England
The set was made up from red, orange, yellow and pink bricks
It contained two small figures, a couple
The couple were not made with regular Lego hands
They had hands that could hold each other
As I began to build the set in the front room with the early
morning curtains closed
The light in the room began to change
New shadows appeared
In the box was a pair of children's sunglasses, and a small
bottle of factor 15 suncream
I put the sunglasses on, applied the suncream to my burning
arms and continued to build
Stepping back from my creation the room was full of unnatural
light
The flowers on the mantelpiece lifted their heads in confusion
Body clocks broken

I fixed the couple's hands together, the man with the raised
yellow circle on his square palm and the woman with the
corresponding indented circle
They stood about a metre from the sunset

It was finished
The pinks and reds were almost soft fuzzy edged Lego bricks
I lowered my head down to the carpet and looked at the faces
of the couple
The setting of the sun reddening their yellowness
Smiles fixed in position, perfectly dressed in skin-tight clothes
Mum, Dad, come and look at this sunset that Granny got me
for Christmas

There was no response
I shouted again
Dad, Mum, come and look at this sunset
I ran through into their bedroom
Come and look at the sunset I've made
What? Oh the Lego
We went back through into the living room and all that remained
were two long red bricks slowly sinking into the carpet
The couple were nowhere to be seen
But Dad, where's it gone?
I want to play with my sunset
With this my Mum entered the room with another box
Rob we forgot to give you this that Father Christmas dropped
off for you
We found it under our bed

I opened it
Another Lego set
The night sky
Bricks of blacks, blues, purples and a small selection of whites
Remember Son, said my Dad, your sunset doubles
as a sunrise

The BBC's David

His full stops are Earths.
His commas are tadpoles,
Tadpoles unaware of what his full stops have to offer
I want to live a life that is worthy of his voiceover
Like a flying fish
A crab that fills the beach with marbles of sand
Or a bird with the ability to mimic the sound of a chainsaw
I would give what I have for him to narrate her dreams for a
single night
Drown me in a raindrop
Accommodate me in a world without walls
Allow me to swim backstroke down the blood vessels
of a blue whale

If the mouth on the face of the Earth were to open
It is his voice I would want to hear

Second-hand Flame

I bought a second-hand push bike with a candle for a front light
I had never ridden a bike by candlelight before
I dreamt of flame flickering against metal traffic
Cycling through candlelit countryside

My main worry was of wax dripping onto my front tyre
Creating a greasy build up that would eventually send me into
a ditch

Upon our first outing the candle went out within one full circle
of my feet on the pedals

Life And Chips Twice Please

He's got a chip on his shoulder
He's got a potato on his shoulder
He's got a bag of Asda smart price potatoes on his shoulder
He's got a brown paper sack of mud laden farmyard potatoes,
a sack that you could fit three babies in if the sack was empty
on his shoulder
He's got a blood red Massey Ferguson tractor with a trailer full
of freshly harvested potatoes on his shoulder
He's got a potato field that is sodden as it has been raining
continuously for the past three weeks on his shoulder
He's got the neighbouring village to the field that is also wet
on his shoulder
He's got the nearest wet city to the wet village on his shoulder,
but the wet city is too big for his shoulder so it is now
sprawling down his back
He's got the wet country on his back
He's got the wet Earth on his back
He's got the wet moon on his back
He's got the wet sun on his back
He's got the wet universe on his back, and a chip on his shoulder

Flight Path

Buzzing around frantically with its tiny pristine engine
The fly forces me to feel lazy
Never has a living being been so accurately named
If we could document the flight paths of flies
Jackson Pollock's paintings would lose all worth
The fly paints its flight path until it dies
The journey from my bedroom to the train station
takes five minutes as the crow flies
And twenty seven years as the fly flies

The Birds And The Bees

The birds are mating with the bees
They are doing it
They are shagging
They are bumming
They are rutting
They are screwing
The birds and the bees are making babies
And the babies are bees with beaks and yellow and black feathers
They live in hives made from twigs
They sting you and have the ability to poo turds of honey

Chess

I look on in amazement as the cheerleaders for the chess match
are arrested for inciting racism

As they are bundled into the back of riot vans a black bishop
shouts
WE ARE GATHERED HERE TODAY TO WIPE OUT
THE WHITES
And from across the board the white pawn asks
What are we doing?
Chess can be quite a racist game sometimes

Underground View

The small boy gazed out the window of the underground train
With his nose pressed up against the glass he could have been
auditioning for a part in the League of Gentlemen
The black soot of the tunnel Papa Lazaroed his reflection

When the train reached a station he turned his back on the view
As if there was nothing to see
His mother saw me looking at him looking
She smiled, leant over to me and whispered
He pretends that the black is bright blue, why don't you?

Milk

This milk tastes like it's off
But it's on
My Cornflakes

Red Sky At Night

With the sun as its painter
The sky had been reworked from blue to red within an evening
hour
I heard people reciting the phrase, red sky at night, and
completing it with their favourite ending
The clouds accepted their temporary colouring, like children
getting their faces painted by a woman they didn't know
Closing my front door I went from out to in with one click of
a latch and remained there until the big quiet bus of morning
pulled up at my window
Opening my bedroom curtains a ripe tomato glow filled my
room
I looked out to see raspberry snow falling from Rothko clouds
A bloody condensed candyfloss had settled on rooftops,
treetops, cartops, roadtops, worldtops
The icing on the Christmas cake had been sabotaged with red
food colouring
Icicles hung like used daggers in this picture postcard of Hell
Rushing out in my dressing gown and slippers I dipped my
fingers into the six inch red to find it was warm,
possessing the same consistency as snow
Children over the road made snowballs as normal
Red hot meteoric cricket ball suns tore through the air
On impact the children dove to ground pretending to bleed
My next door neighbours had built a snowman
The devil of the snowman world
His button coals warmed, plugged into the alien weather
This was the first time the red snow had fallen to Earth
But I was aware that the white snow had a first time too

IF IT'S RAINING
SUNS,
IT'S STILL
RAINING.

Conkers

It was a crisp Sunday morning in autumn as I walked across the Great Yorkshire Moors with the Devil.

Can we stop for a rest soon? Whined the Devil, my feet hurt and I want to sit down to eat the picnic.
You shouldn't have worn those ridiculous shoes, I snapped. Let's walk up to that Horse Chestnut tree, then we can sit down. As we approached the tree the Devil ran excitedly ahead and sat down amongst the solid twisting roots.
That's better, he said, removing his shoes. I sat down on the fallen leaves and took the packed lunch from my rucksack. What have you put in my sandwiches? Asked the Devil. You do know that if you have made me something I do not like you are going to be completely cursed forever.
Relax, I made you your favourite, Golden Eagle and marshmallow on Mighty White with the crusts cut off.
He didn't say anything and snatched the sandwich, burning my hand in the process, he then took a huge bite. He closed his eyes and put his head back against the tree, swallowing hard. I took a bite from my chicken spread on brown, it was OK at best.

It has nothing to do with me you know, all this carnage, said the Devil with his tiny eyes now firmly open, it's difficult when you get blamed for everything.
It seems you people take the thickest shoelaces you can find, tie big knots in the end and thread your hearts onto them like conkers. Walking around forever trying to find someone to have a contest with.
That's fair enough, I replied, but I brought sensible shoes this morning, and you however, did not.

Blue Ball

I hold my hands up to the sky
A cloud swims through my fingers and continues on its
journey
Bringing my arms back down I notice that the final thirds of
my fingers are shelled with blue
As if I've been dipping my digits in the melted wax of the
upside down candles of the sky
I have Smurf like fingertips
I peel the sky from the ends of my fingers and roll it into a
primary coloured chocolate-all-the-way-through Maltester

So, that's the colour of the sky

I feel a raindrop, then another, and then it begins to rain
The ball of sky slowly turns grey
I drop it
It disappears into the overcast pavement

99 On The Floor

When I was a child I thought adults knew what was going on
I thought they knew why people do what they do
Why certain things exist in the world
At least when I was a child I had an excuse
Sometimes I think to myself, if I was a baby I would be crying
now
There is a reason why a child bursts into tears when he drops
his ice cream
Because it seems unfair
If I drop my ice cream as an adult, I don't cry
The shock of it is gone, I have dropped too many ice creams
And have learnt that worse things happen

Dust

I became aware that you were a nasty piece of work when I came round to your single bed flat. The room needed dusting. I noticed that your dust didn't coat things evenly like other people's dust. Your dust fell and formed letters, and the letters formed words and the words formed sentences that I couldn't possibly repeat.

Fish

Fish in the sea, why do get to be so free?
Fish in the bowl, why do you get to be so gold?
Fish in the supermarket, why do you get to be so dead?
Fish in my stomach, why do you get to be so nutritious?

The Season Family

The frail winter and the ancient summer are a couple
Together since the starting gun of time went BANG!
They walk the Earth needy only of each other

Winter walks with a worn grazed icicle crutch
Summer is aided by an aged zimmer frame of hairy orange light

As they walk the land they conjure up life and death in equal
measures
Summer's piercing eyes reflected in the black ice of winter's face
As a regular couple each have a side of the bed
They each have a side of the sky

Once a year winter gives his leaf free tree hand to summer
As she takes it in her voluptuous bosom of blossom spring is born

Once a year summer gives her leaf clothed tree hand to winter
As he takes it in his naked structure autumn is born

Winter and summer, man and wife
Spring and autumn, sister and brother

The Dare

The snowman took his hat and scarf off
Left them at the side
Dived into the indoor swimming pool
Within two seconds he became translucent
He got half way through a crawl of front crawl before slushing
to blue
I can still see his side on face taking that breath
Coal sank leaving inconsistent wet black vertical vapour trails
His smile settled on the pool bed in slow motion
A carrot bobbed into the air and rested on the surface
It must have been a hollow carrot
The water level increased by one millimetre
The ghost of the snowman now free to swim laps of his afterlife

Yellow Orange

I am sat next to an elderly man on the train to York. He has been shaking a bottle of fresh orange juice for the past ten minutes. Inspecting it closely after each vigorous shake. Is this shaking grown from experience? Does he know something about drinking orange juice that I do not? As we travel through the afternoon countryside he continues to shake. It makes nearly no sound as it is unopened and four millimetres from full. Sweat drips from anywhere it can find an outlet. Just as we pull into Doncaster he stops. The look on his face is one of 'equation solved'.

He attempts to unscrew the lid and it won't open. He tries harder and harder and harder. Clamping the round green lid between his teeth the lid comes loose. His eyes shut and they don't open again until the lid and bottle are two separate pieces of plastic. I look at the colour of the liquid. A cheddar coloured sun lemon.

Opening his eyes he asks,

Would you like some of my drink?

What is it?

It's orange juice, he says.

Yes please.

I take the bottle in my hand, the bottle that has been the focus of my entire journey and begin to drink. It tastes like warm orange juice that has been shaken for an hour and a half.

It's orange juice, I say.

He looks at me for a second and begins to smile. A smile broad and glistening with white and pink.

Isn't it beautiful? He asks me, his face now built from bricks of happiness.

I am 86 years old and I only tasted orange juice for the first time yesterday. Have you tried it before?

Yes I have.

FULL STOPS
ARE THE
BEAUTY SPOTS
OF SENTENCES.